11+
Non-verbal Reasoning
Three-dimensional Technique

WORKBOOK 3

Dr Stephen C Curran

with Natalie Knowles

Edited by Andrea Richardson & Katrina MacKay

This book belongs to

Accelerated Education Publications Ltd

Contents

Chapter Fourteen
3D ROTATION
1. Three-dimensional Shapes
a. What is a 3D Shape?

A shape is called **Three-dimensional** or **3D** if it has three dimensions or can be measured in three directions. It has a width, a depth and a height. Each 3D shape is made up of faces (flat sides), edges (where faces meet) and vertices (corners where faces and edges meet).

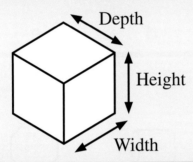

The width, height and depth of this shape can be measured.

Example: | Identify which shape is three-dimensional.

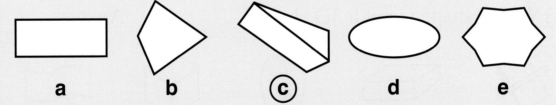

Shape **c** is the only shape with three dimensions.

Example: | Identify which shape is not three-dimensional.

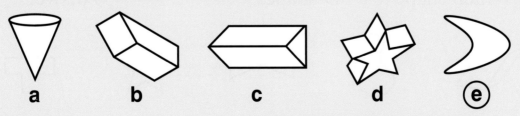

Shape **e** is the only shape with only two dimensions.

Exercise 14: 1 Answer the following questions:

1) Which shape is a 3D shape?   Answer ____

   a   b   c   d   e

2) Which shape is not a 3D shape?   Answer ____

   a   b   c   d   e

3) Which shape is a 3D shape?   Answer ____

   a   b   c   d   e

4) Which shape is not a 3D shape?   Answer ____

   a   b   c   d   e

5) Which shape is a 3D shape?   Answer ____

   a   b   c   d   e

6) Which shape is not a 3D shape?   Answer ____

   a   b   c   d   e

7) Which shape is a 3D shape?   Answer ____

   a   b   c   d   e

8) Which shape is not a 3D shape?   Answer ____

   a   b   c   d   e

9) Which shape is a 3D shape?   Answer ____

   a   b   c   d   e

10) Which shape is not a 3D shape?   Answer ____

   a   b   c   d   e

Score

b. 3D Palette of Shapes
(i) Standard 3D Shapes Palette

These are geometrically defined 3D shapes.

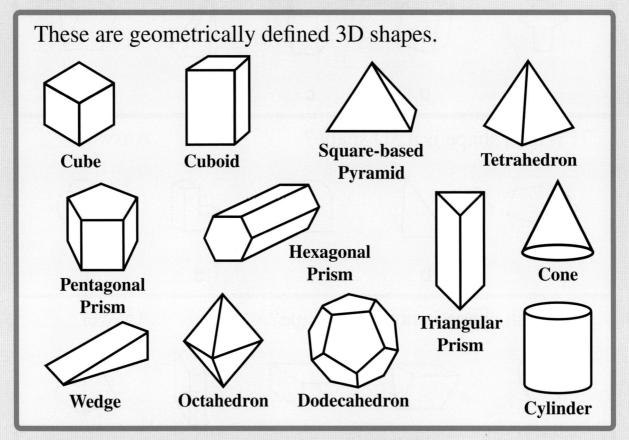

Cube   Cuboid   Square-based Pyramid   Tetrahedron

Pentagonal Prism   Hexagonal Prism   Triangular Prism   Cone

Wedge   Octahedron   Dodecahedron   Cylinder

(ii) Specialist 3D Shapes Palette

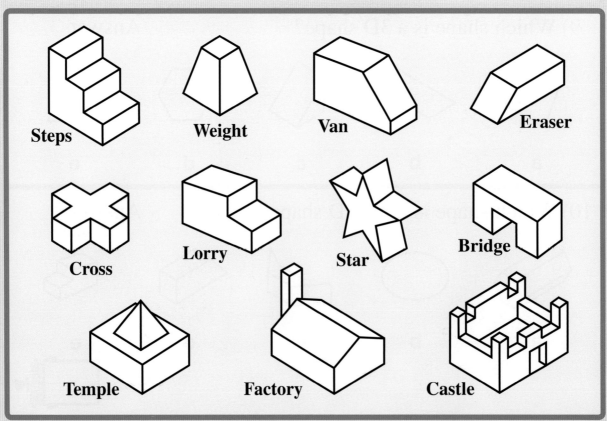

Steps   Weight   Van   Eraser

Cross   Lorry   Star   Bridge

Temple   Factory   Castle

Exercise 14: 2 Name the following shapes:

1)

_____

2)

_____

3)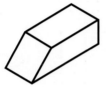

_____

4)

_____

5)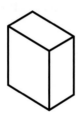

_____

6)

_____

7)

_____

8)

_____

9)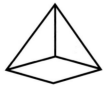

_____

10)

_____

2. Types of 3D Questions
a. Viewer Rotation

Viewer Rotation means imagining physically moving to various points around a shape and viewing it from each new position. It is the same as rotating **90°** at a time around the shape to look at it from different points of view.

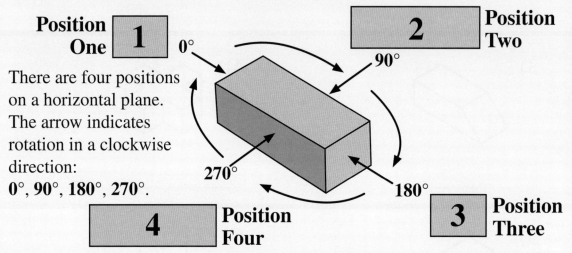

Position One | **1** | 0°

2 | **Position Two**

There are four positions on a horizontal plane. The arrow indicates rotation in a clockwise direction:
0°, 90°, 180°, 270°.

90°

270°

4 | **Position Four**

180°

3 | **Position Three**

When moving on a flat horizontal plane, there are four positions this Cuboid can be viewed from. These viewpoints are shown here two-dimensionally to avoid complication.

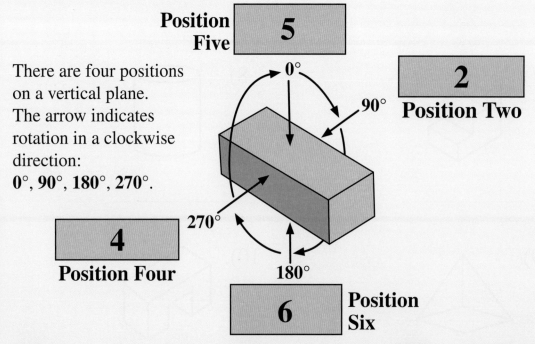

Position Five | **5**

2 | **Position Two**

There are four positions on a vertical plane. The arrow indicates rotation in a clockwise direction:
0°, 90°, 180°, 270°.

0°

90°

270°

4 | **Position Four**

180°

6 | **Position Six**

When moving on an upright vertical plane **90°** each time, two more views (Position 5 and 6) are shown above and below.

Example: Identify the correct view of this shape as indicated by the arrow.

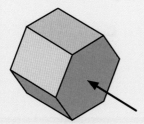

Imagine moving around the shape into the same place as the arrow and viewing the shape from this position. What can be seen?

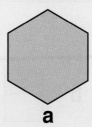   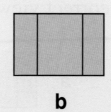   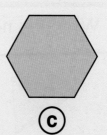

a   **b**   **ⓒ**

It must be a Hexagon, which rules out **b**. The Hexagon is flat at the top so **a** cannot be the answer, meaning that **c** is the right answer.

Example: Identify which of these options is not a correct view of the shape.

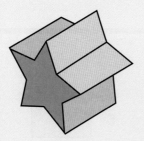

Carefully examine each option and imagine moving into a position around the shape to where that particular view might be seen.

ⓐ   **b**   **c**

If the shape is viewed from the front or back we will see **c**. If it is viewed from the side or top we will see **b**. However, **a** has been squashed so it is not a correct view of the shape, meaning **a** is the right answer.

Exercise 14: 3   Answer the following questions:

1) Which is a correct view?

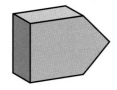   a    b   c

_____

2) Which is not a correct view?

   a   b   c

_____

3) Which is a correct view?

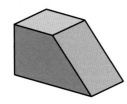   a   b   c

_____

4) Which is not a correct view?

   a   b   c

_____

5) Which is a correct view?

   a   b   c

_____

6) Which is not a correct view?

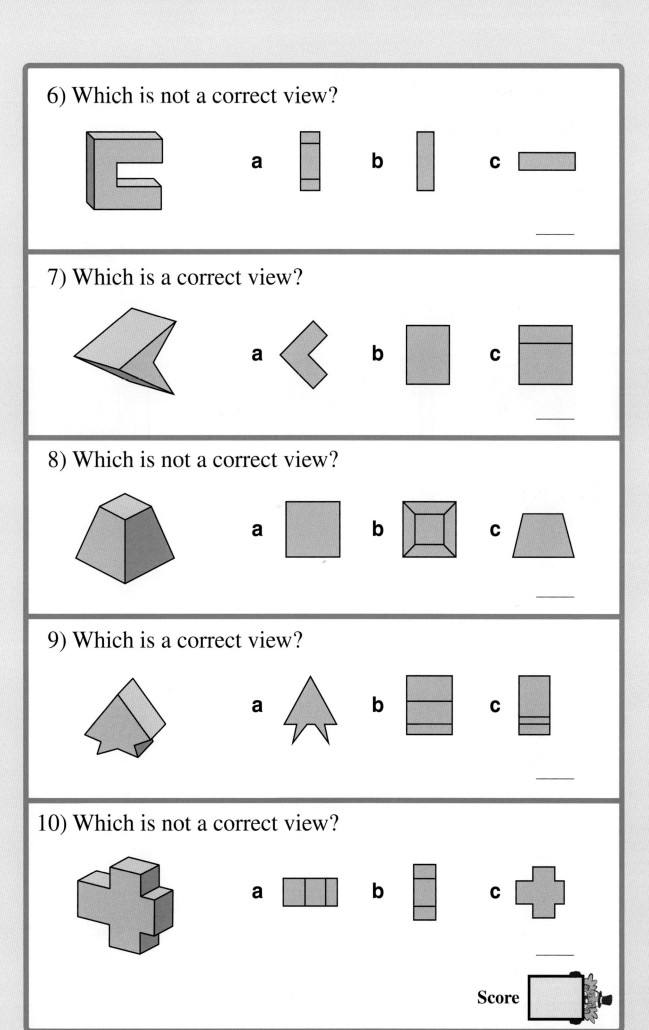

a   b   c

7) Which is a correct view?

a   b   c

8) Which is not a correct view?

a   b   c

9) Which is a correct view?

a   b   c

10) Which is not a correct view?

a   b   c

Score

b. Rotational View

Rotational View occurs when we imagine the given shape rotating from its original position into a new position. These rotations can occur on a horizontal or a vertical plane or a combination of both planes.

This Cuboid has been rotated into a number of different positions.

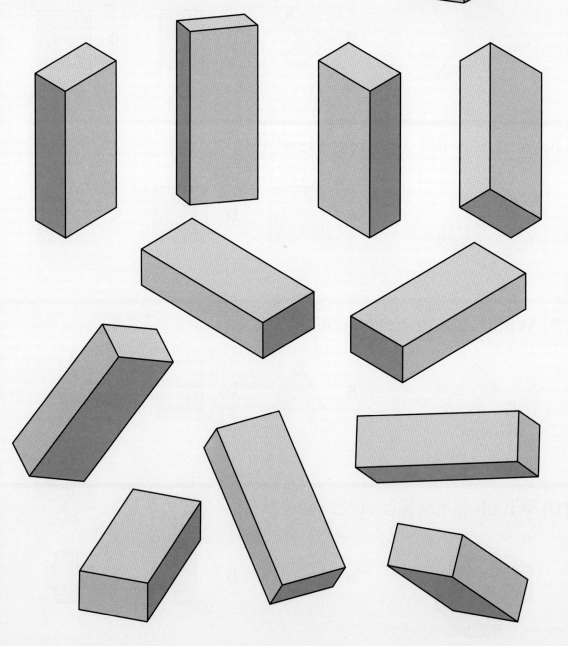

The most important thing is to be able to recognise the given shape in whatever new position it has been rotated to.

Example: Identify which 3D shape is a rotation of the Test Shape.

Imagine the various options rotating into the same position as the Test Shape. Check also that the various shapes are the same as the Test Shape as it may have been altered in some way.

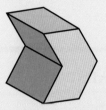 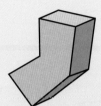 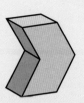 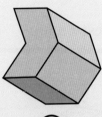

Test Shape　　　　**a**　　　　**b**　　　　ⓒ

Option **b** appears to be correct but its depth is shallower. Option **a** is a completely different shape. Option **c** has been rotated into a different position but it is the same shape and is therefore the correct answer.

Example: Identify which 3D shape is not a rotation of the Test Shape.

Imagine the various options rotating into the same position as the Test Shape. Look out for one shape that has been altered in some way and is not a rotation of the Test Shape.

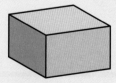 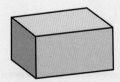 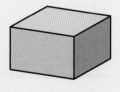 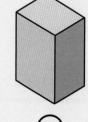

Test Shape　　　　**a**　　　　**b**　　　　ⓒ

Options **a** and **b** are rotations and are the same shape as the Test Shape. However, the face of option **c** is thinner and longer and it is not a rotation of the Test Shape. This means that option **c** is the correct answer.

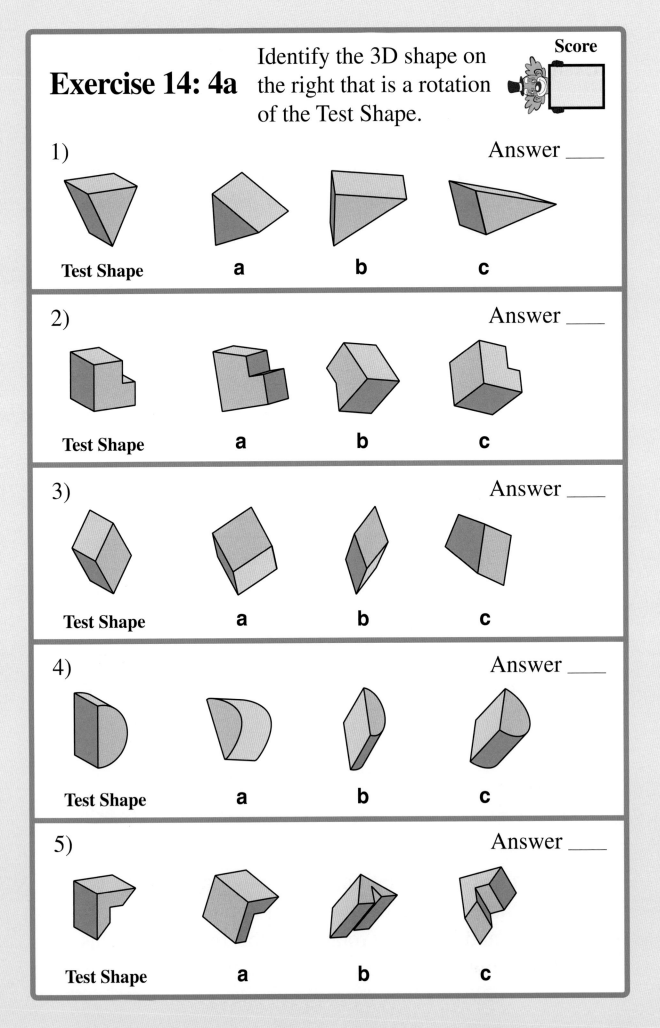

Exercise 14: 4a

Identify the 3D shape on the right that is a rotation of the Test Shape.

1) Answer ___

Test Shape   a   b   c

2) Answer ___

Test Shape   a   b   c

3) Answer ___

Test Shape   a   b   c

4) Answer ___

Test Shape   a   b   c

5) Answer ___

Test Shape   a   b   c

Exercise 14: 4b

Identify the 3D shape on the right that is not a rotation of the Test Shape.

6)   Answer ____

Test Shape   **a**   **b**   **c**

7)   Answer ____

Test Shape   **a**   **b**   **c**

8)   Answer ____

Test Shape   **a**   **b**   **c**

9)   Answer ____

Test Shape   **a**   **b**   **c**

10)   Answer ____

Test Shape   **a**   **b**   **c**

Chapter Fifteen
VIEWER ROTATION

The concept of **Viewer Rotation** involves imagining physically moving around a shape and viewing it from a new position.

The following types of activities involve viewer rotation:
- **Counting Faces on 3D Shapes**
- **Isometric Projection**
- **Plan Views using Blocks**

1. Counting Faces on 3D Shapes

When a three-dimensional shape is drawn in two dimensions some of the faces, edges and vertices are visible. The others remain unseen as they are on the other side of the shape.

Standard 3D shapes are geometrically defined and are used in mathematics. These shapes are regularly encountered as objects in everyday life, so we are usually aware of how many faces they have.

For example the Cube shape, which has six faces, is used for dice or children's building blocks.

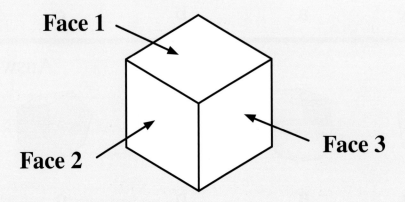

There are only three visible faces on this Cube when it is drawn in two dimensions.

In order to calculate the total number of faces on any 3D shape we have to envisage what is on the other side of the shape. This can be done by imagining the shape has rotated, but there is also a simpler way to solve this.

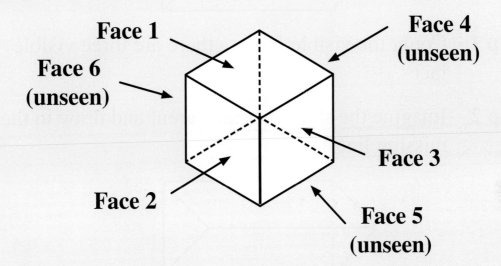

In this second depiction of the Cube it has been drawn as if it is transparent (see-through) and the invisible faces, edges and vertices have been indicated by dotted lines. However, this kind of assistance is not usually given in questions involving 3D shapes.

When the dotted lines are drawn in we can imagine seeing through the shape as if it is transparent. The faces, edges and vertices, which are normally unseen, become visible. This means we do not have to imagine the shape rotating.

After the dotted lines have been drawn in it is easy to see that a Cube has a total of six faces.

However, working out how many faces a non-standard or specialist 3D shape has is more difficult as we come across these types of shapes less often.

This is a skill that has to be developed through practice.

Example: | Count the number of faces on this Triangular Prism.

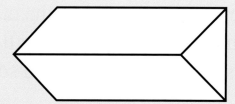

Step 1 - Count the visible faces – there are three visible faces.

Step 2 - Imagine the shape is transparent and draw in the missing lines.

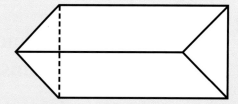

Step 3 - Count the unseen faces – there are two unseen faces.

Step 4 - Add the visible and unseen faces – 3 + 2 faces.

Answer: The Triangular Prism has a total of **5** faces.

Exercise 15: 1

Count the number of faces on the following 3D shapes:

1)

_____ faces

2)

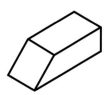

_____ faces

3)

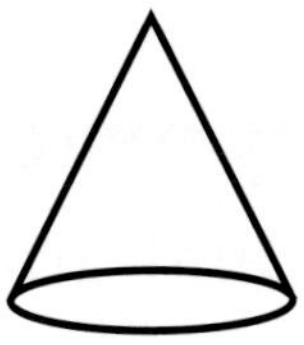

_____ faces

4)

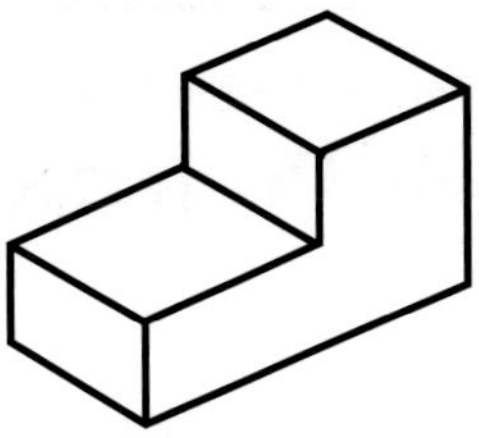

_____ faces

5)

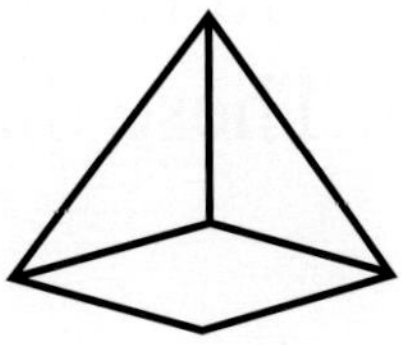

_____ faces

6)

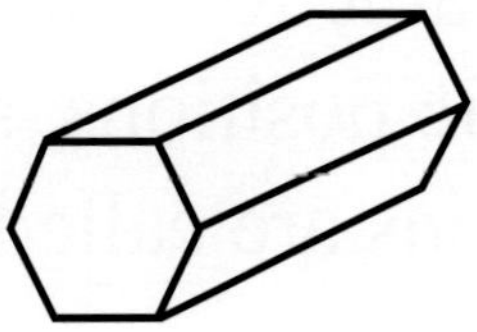

_____ faces

7)

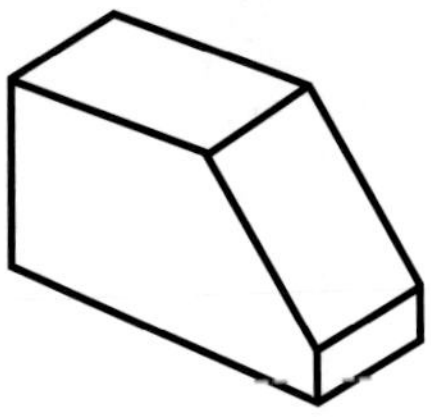

_____ faces

8)

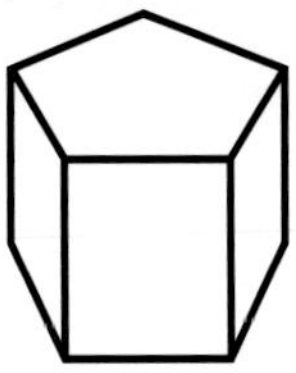

_____ faces

9)

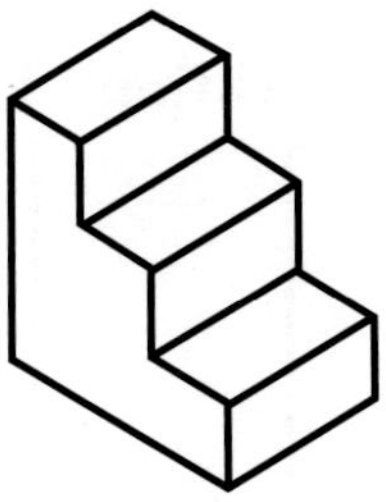

_____ faces

10)

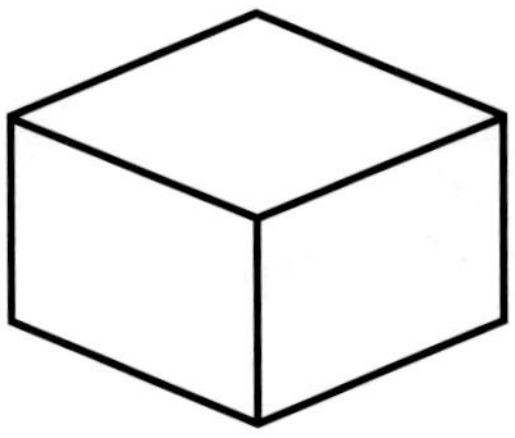

_____ faces

Score

2. Isometric Projection

Isometric Projection is a method for visually representing three-dimensional objects with two-dimensional drawings. A 3D shape can be denoted by drawing from three specific planes: **top elevation** or **plan view**, **front elevation** and **side elevation**. If a shape is viewed from the back, both the front and side elevations can be denoted as **rear elevations**.

Drawing accurate 2D representations of an object involves being able to imagine observing the object from these three specific positions, so it is a form of rotation. These three positions are called **Orthographic Views**.

Although the object does not actually rotate, the viewer of the object has to imagine seeing it from a particular angle. In other words, the observer of the shape must rotate around the shape in their imagination.

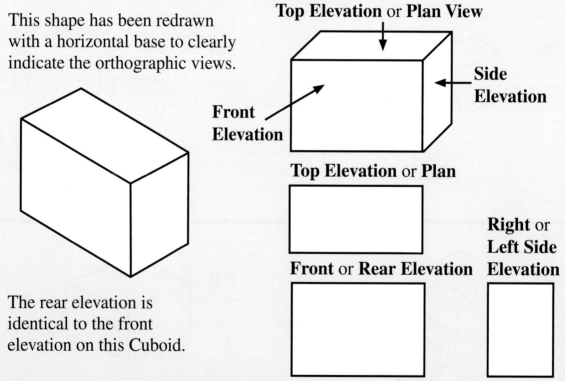

This shape has been redrawn with a horizontal base to clearly indicate the orthographic views.

Top Elevation or **Plan View**

Side Elevation

Front Elevation

Top Elevation or **Plan**

Front or **Rear Elevation**

Right or **Left Side Elevation**

The rear elevation is identical to the front elevation on this Cuboid.

This gives three different views. The Cuboid can be seen from above (top elevation or plan view), viewed square on (front elevation) or observed from one side (side elevation).

Pop out the net on page 4 of the Supplementary Material and make the shape.

Example: Study this 3D shape and select the correct orthographic projection that corresponds to the view indicated by the arrow.

a   b   c   d

Imagine moving around the shape to be positioned in line with the direction of the arrow. What would be seen from this position? Thinking in this way will help select the correct isometric projection.

d

Answer: **d** - This is what would be seen if the shape were viewed from this position. It is a top elevation or plan view.

Exercise 15: 2

Study the following 3D shapes and select the correct orthographic projection that corresponds to the view indicated by the arrow:

a   b

1)

c   d

This orthographic view is a _____ elevation.

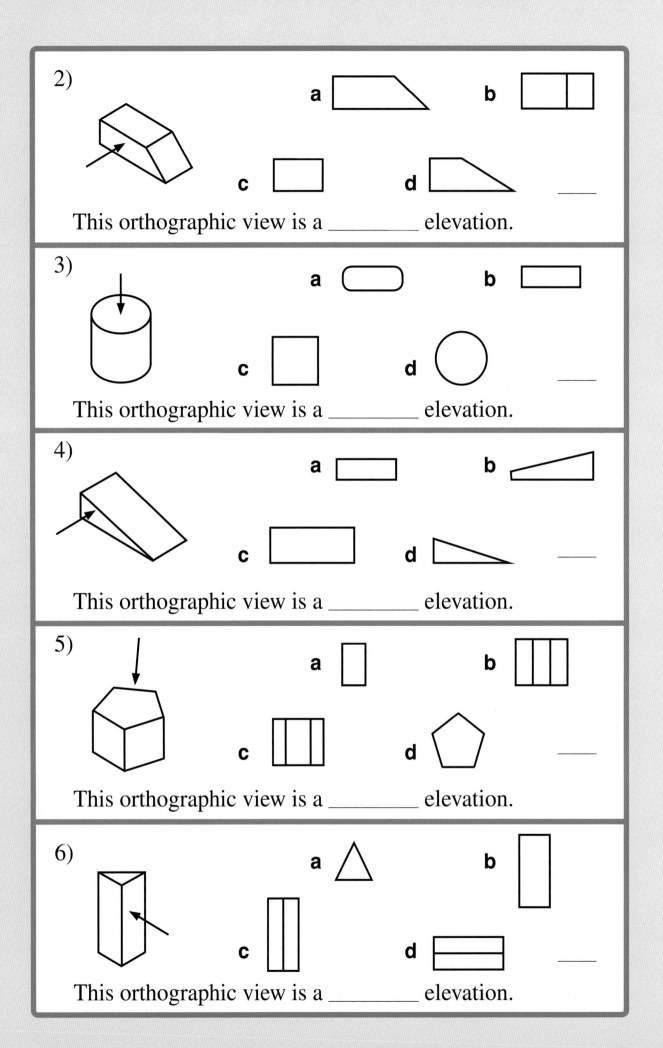

2)

a

b

c

d _____

This orthographic view is a _____ elevation.

3)

a

b

c

d _____

This orthographic view is a _____ elevation.

4)

a

b

c

d _____

This orthographic view is a _____ elevation.

5)

a

b

c

d _____

This orthographic view is a _____ elevation.

6)

a

b

c

d _____

This orthographic view is a _____ elevation.

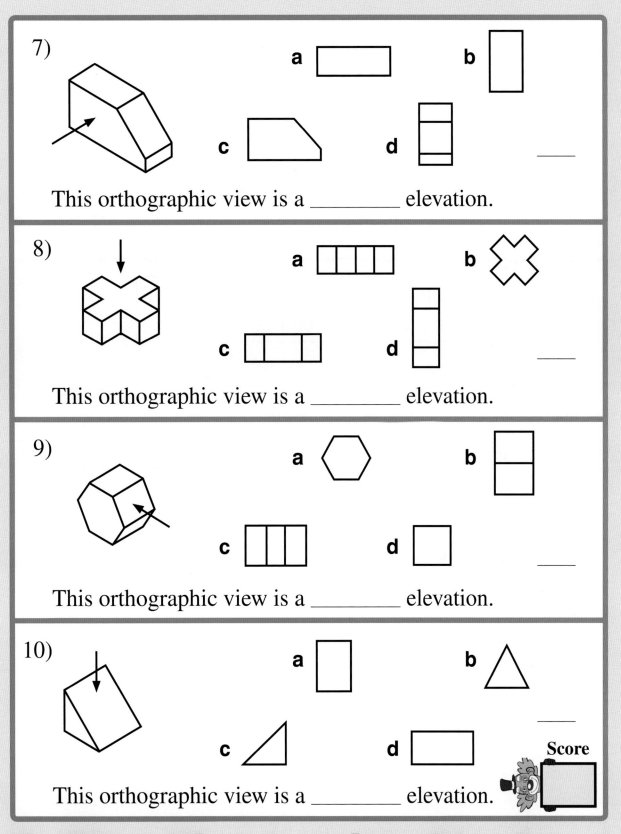

7)   a   b

c   d   _____

This orthographic view is a _____ elevation.

8)   a   b

c   d   _____

This orthographic view is a _____ elevation.

9)   a   b

c   d   _____

This orthographic view is a _____ elevation.

10)   a   b

c   d   **Score**

This orthographic view is a _____ elevation.

3. Plan Views using Blocks

One form of question makes use of cubes or blocks to construct **composite figures** from which a top elevation or plan view is drawn. It is then necessary to select the correct top elevation or plan view from a series of given options. Block or cube composite figures and their associated top elevation or plan views can take many and varied forms:

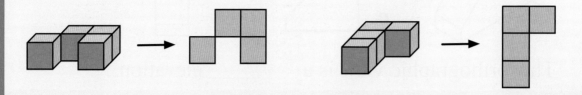

Example: Identify the correct top elevation or plan view of this composite figure.

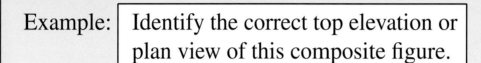

Test Figure   a   b   c   d

The Test Figure is a 3D view of the figure. In order to identify the correct top elevation or plan view, the viewer must imagine seeing the figure from above. This means the viewer must imagine rotating into the position of the arrow (viewer rotation) and looking down at the figure.

Imagine moving to this position and looking down at the composite figure from above.

Options **a**, **b** and **c** are are not top elevation or plan views of the Test Figure. Black fill squares are incorrectly placed and white fill dashed squares show squares that are missing.

d is the correct answer.

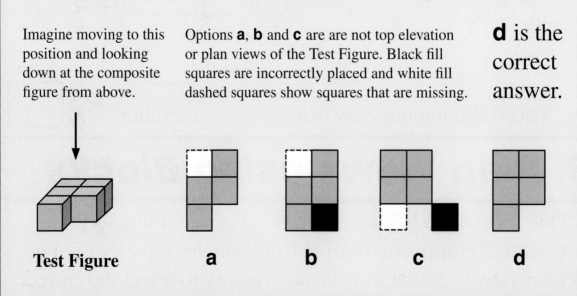

Test Figure   a   b   c   d

Exercise 15: 3

Identify the correct top elevation or plan view of the composite figure.

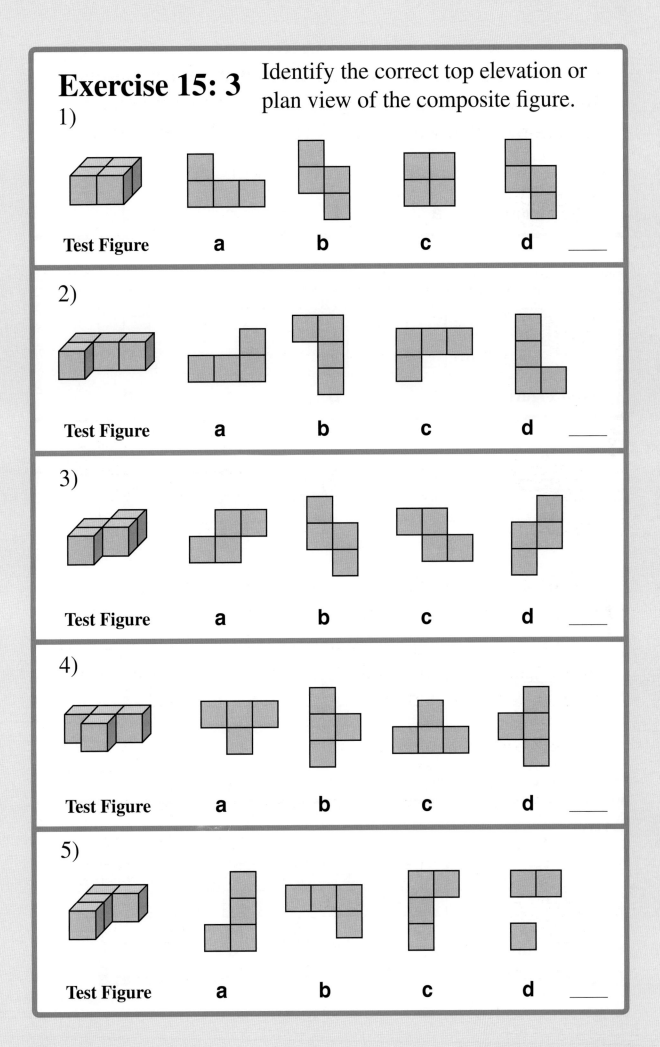

1)

Test Figure   **a**   **b**   **c**   **d** ____

2)

Test Figure   **a**   **b**   **c**   **d** ____

3)

Test Figure   **a**   **b**   **c**   **d** ____

4)

Test Figure   **a**   **b**   **c**   **d** ____

5)

Test Figure   **a**   **b**   **c**   **d** ____

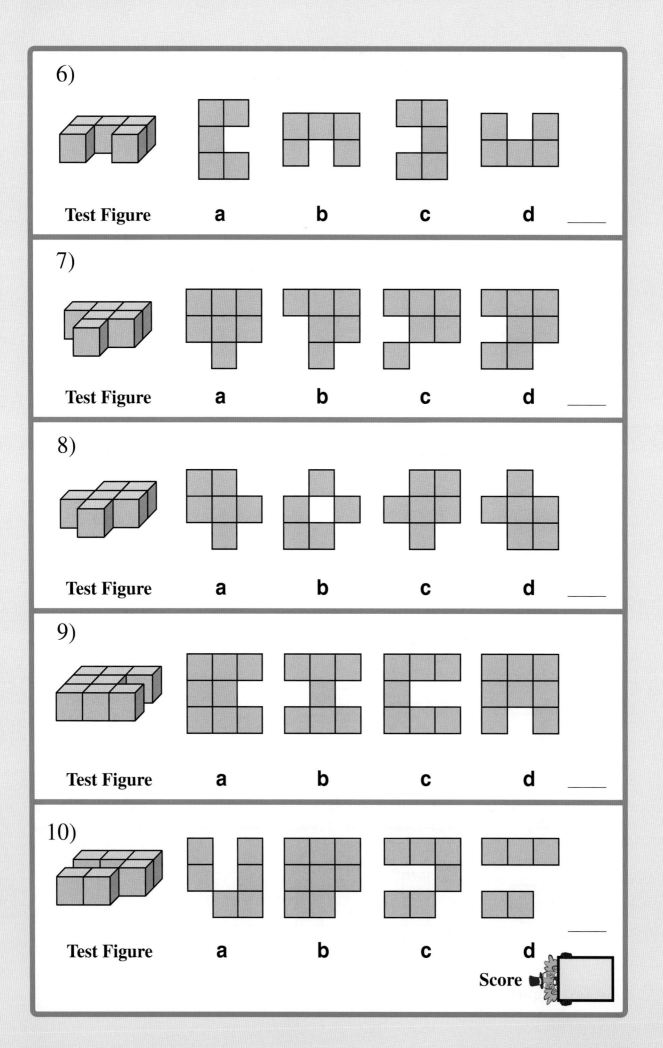

6)

Test Figure   **a**   **b**   **c**   **d**   _____

7)

Test Figure   **a**   **b**   **c**   **d**   _____

8)

Test Figure   **a**   **b**   **c**   **d**   _____

9)

Test Figure   **a**   **b**   **c**   **d**   _____

10)

Test Figure   **a**   **b**   **c**   **d**   _____

Score

4. Counting Blocks

This type of question also consists of composite figures constructed from cubes or blocks, which must be counted. This involves imagining cubes or blocks that are present in the composite figure but cannot be seen. In these exercises, assume that the composite figures are solid and built from the ground up. Therefore all blocks that cannot be seen must be counted.

Example: How many blocks are there in the figure?

Step 1 - Imagine separating the shape into layers of blocks. This shape logically breaks into two horizontal layers. It is now easier to visualise the hidden blocks.

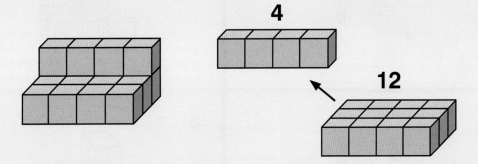

Step 2 - Count the blocks in each layer separately, including the hidden blocks that were originally concealed.

Step 3 - Add the layers together. **4 + 12 = 16**

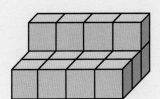

Answer: There are **16** blocks in the figure.

Exercise 15: 4 How many blocks are there in the figure?

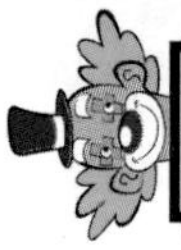

Score

1)

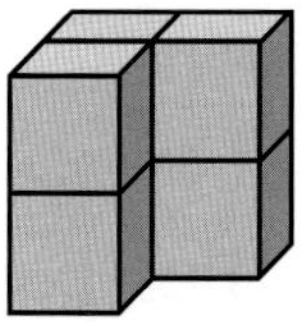

______

2)

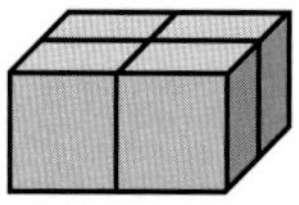

______

3)

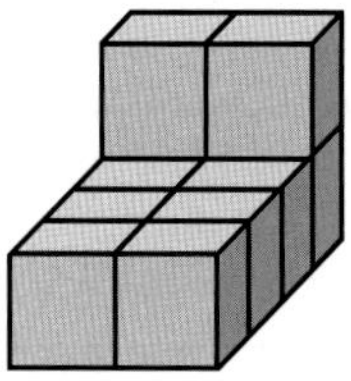

______

4)

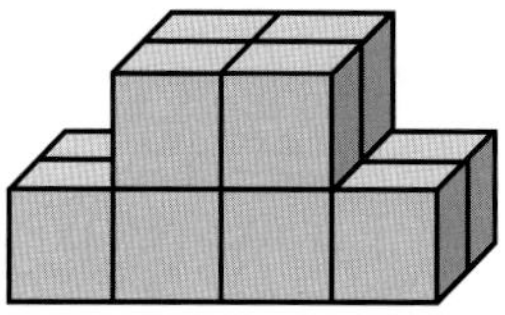

______

5)

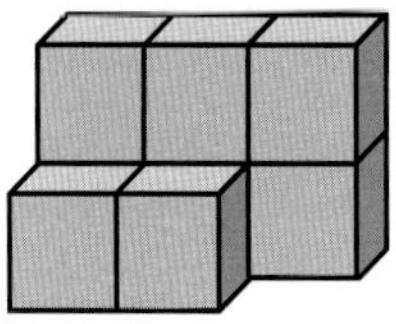

______

6)

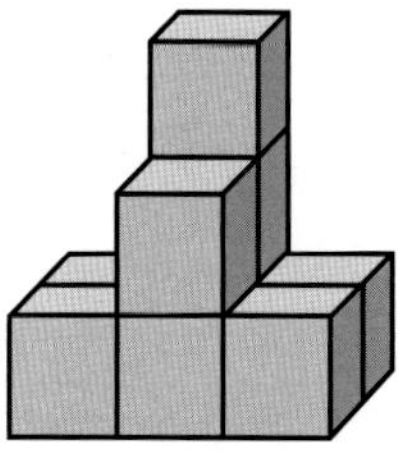

______

7)

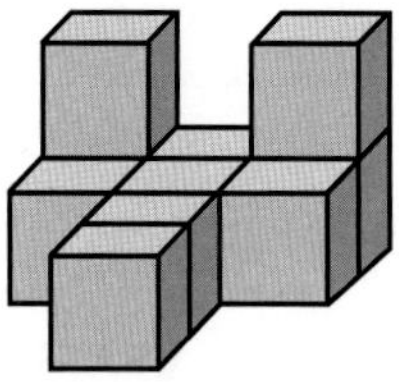

______

8)

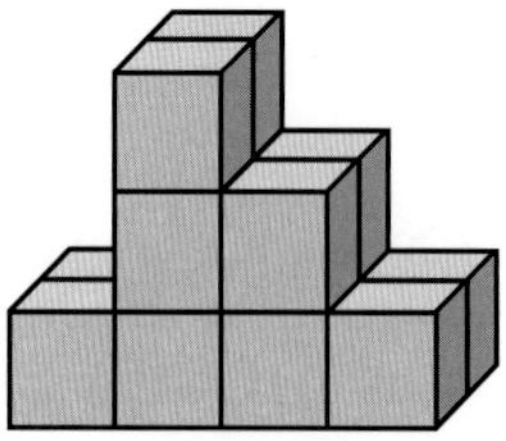

______

9)

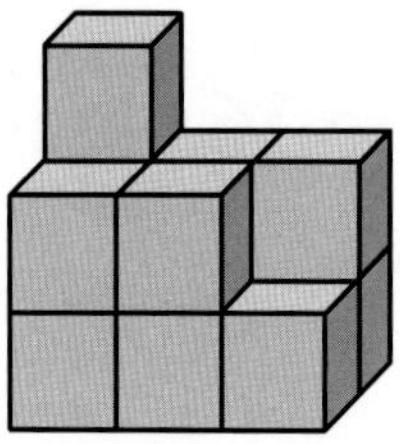

______

10)

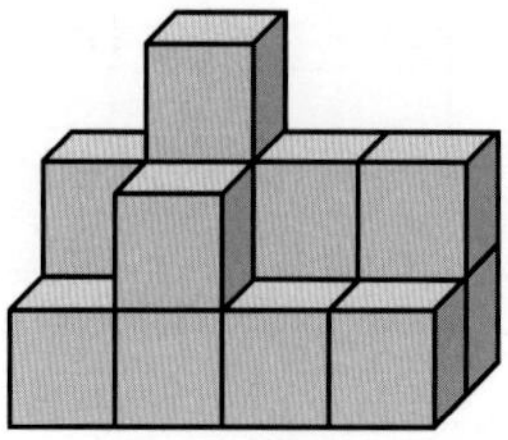

______

Chapter Sixteen
ROTATIONAL VIEW

Rotational View is the concept of imagining the given shape rotating into a new position.

The following types of activities involve rotational view:

Shapes and Nets • Composite Figures
Rotating Figures

1. Shapes and Nets

A **Net** is a two-dimensional pattern that can be folded up to become a solid three-dimensional shape. A standard 3D shape, such as a Cube, can only be constructed from a net that has certain faces positioned correctly on the net.

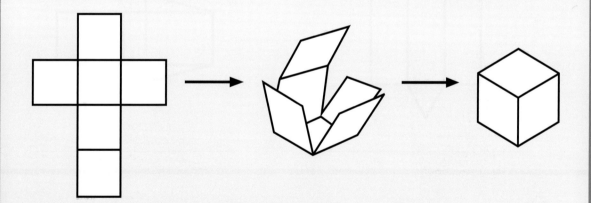

Four of the faces of this cube net are in one line and two protrude either side in order to be able to build this Cube. As the cube net is folded up the two faces that protrude fold in to complete the Cube.

> Use the pop-out cube nets on page 6 of the Supplementary Material to construct your own 3D shapes.

Cubes can also be constructed from other nets:

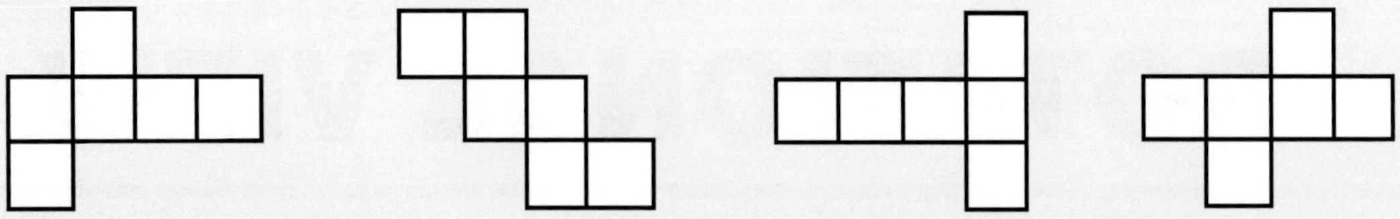

Exercise 16: 1   Name the three-dimensional shape.

1)

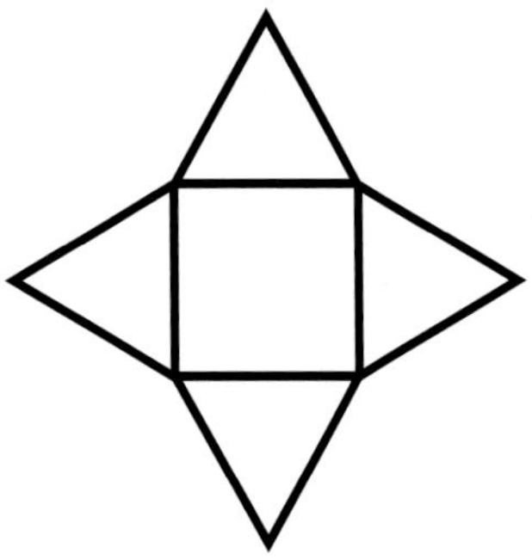

_____

2)

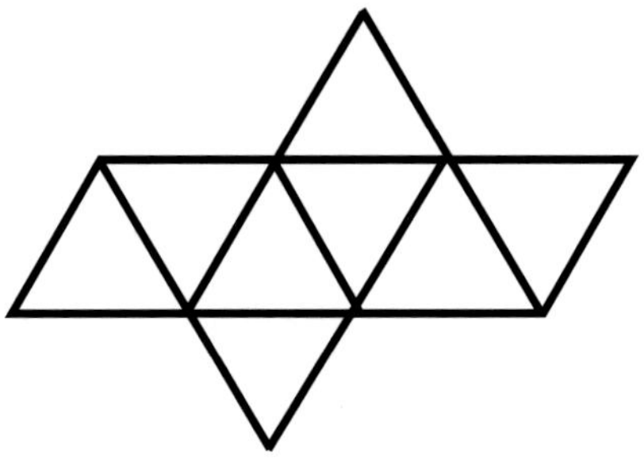

_____

3)

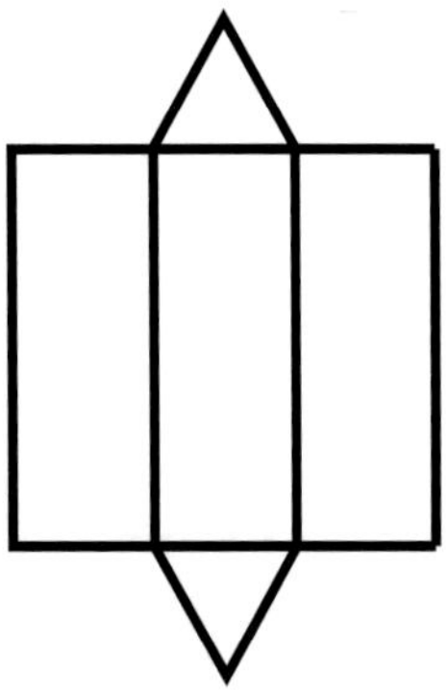

_____

4)

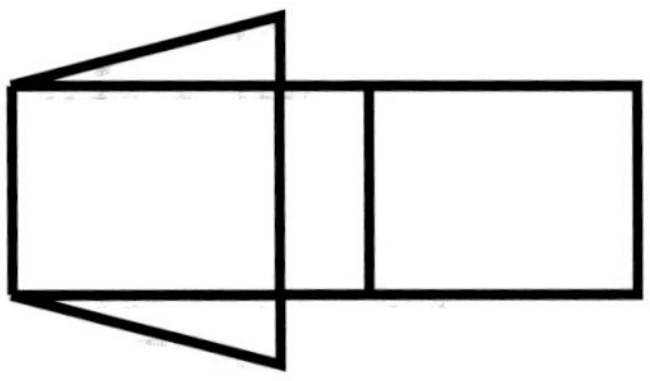

_____

5)

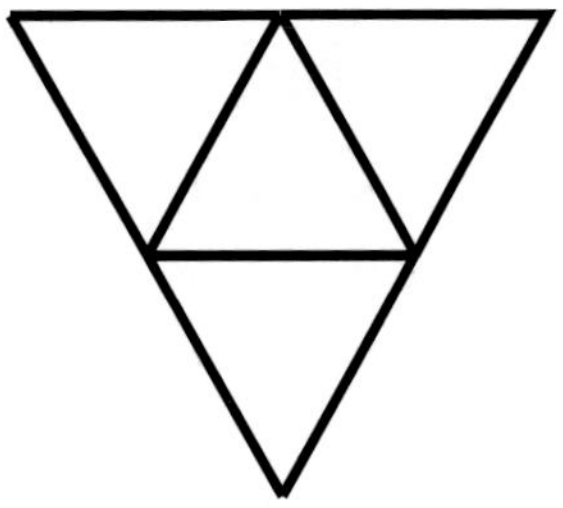

_____

Use the pop-out nets from pages 1-5 of the Supplementary Material and form the three-dimensional shapes.

6)

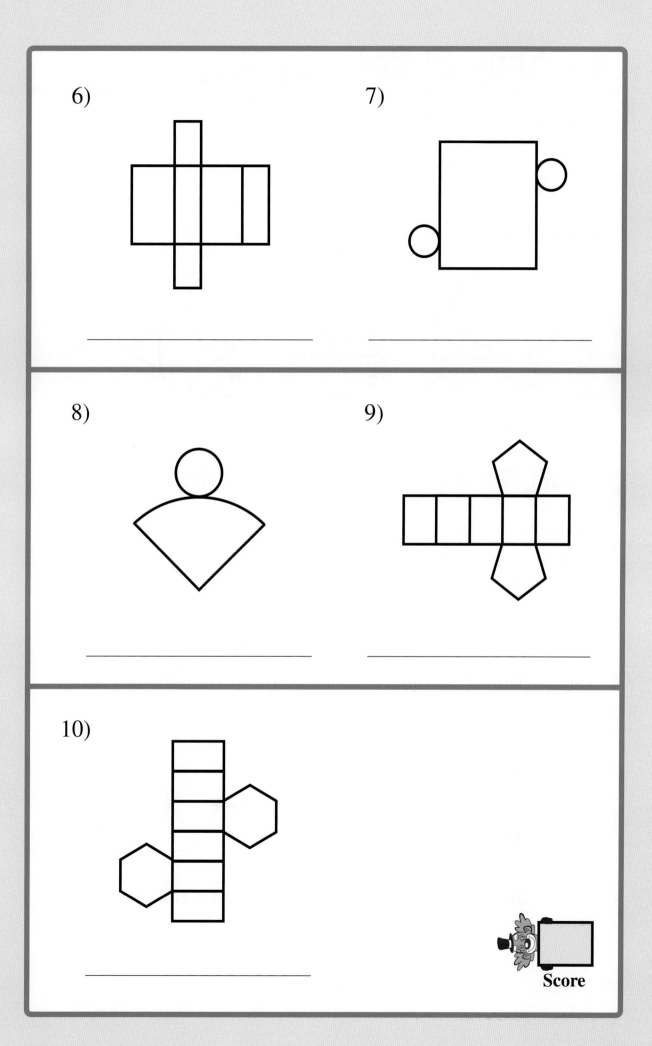

_____

7)

_____

8)

_____

9)

_____

10)

_____

Score

a. Shape to Net

Example: | Study this 3D shape and select the correct net that it can be constructed from.

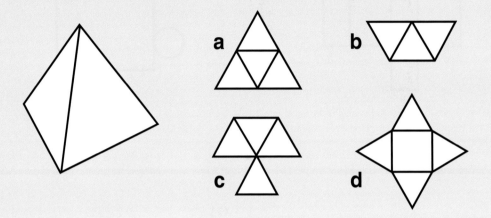

a

b

c

d

Imagine folding up each net in turn to see if it will construct the shape, or imagine the shape itself unfolding:

- There are not enough faces on net **b** to make the shape
- Once folded the faces in **c** will not fit together properly
- Net **d** makes a Square-based Pyramid - the wrong shape

If three of the four faces of net **a** are folded up, or the Tetrahedron is unfolded, we can see this must be the correct answer. This is indicated in the diagram below:

A Tetrahedron can also be constructed from this net:

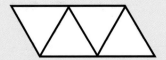

Exercise 16: 2a

Identify the correct net that will construct the 3D shape:

1)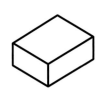

a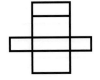

b

c

d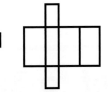

2)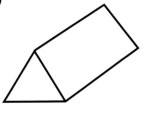

a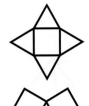

b

c

d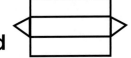

3)

a

b

c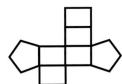

d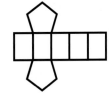

4)

a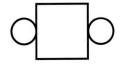

b

c

d

5)

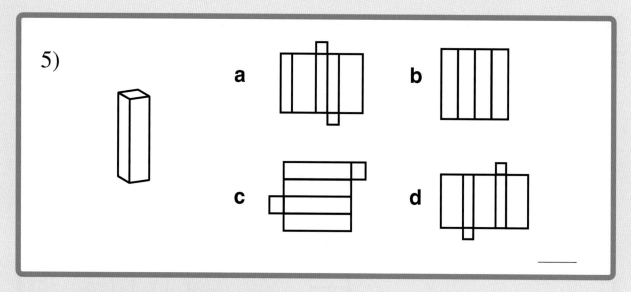

b. Net to Shape

Example: Study this net and select the correct 3D shape it will construct.

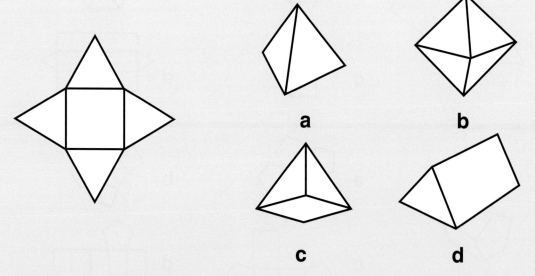

Imagine the net folding in. Examine each 3D shape in turn to see if it matches. The diagram indicates the folds:

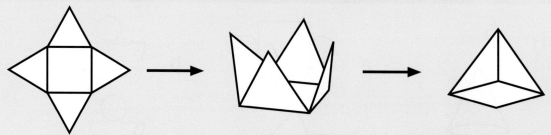

Pop out the net on page 1 of the Supplementary Material and fold as shown to create the 3D shape.

- Shape **a** is a Tetrahedron and does not have square faces
- Shape **b** is an Octahedron and has too many faces
- Shape **d** is a Triangular Prism and has three rectangular faces

If four of the faces of the net are folded in they will make a Square-based Pyramid so the answer must be shape **c**.

The Square-based Pyramid can also be contructed from other nets such as the one below:

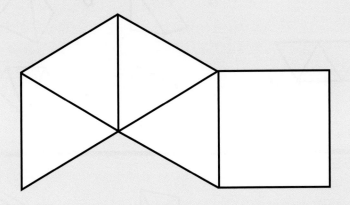

Exercise 16: 2b

Examine the following nets and select the correct 3D shapes they construct:

6)

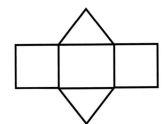

a   b

c   d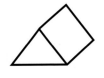

7)

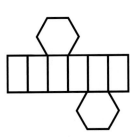

a  b

c   d

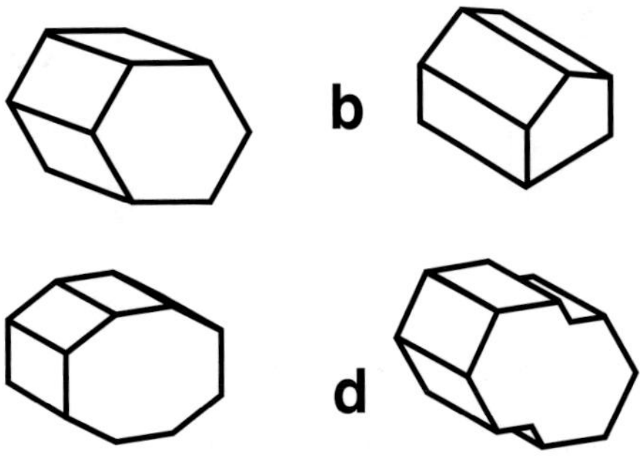

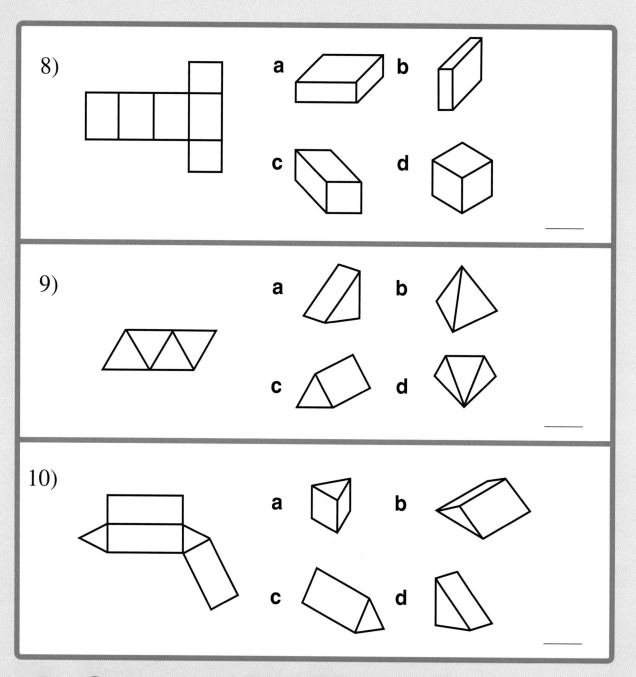

2. Composite Figures

Composite Figures are constructed from a palette of 3D shapes based on cubes and block shapes which are rotated and joined up.

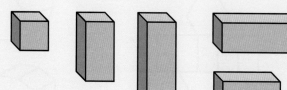

The 3D shapes can face right as well as left.

Example: | Identify which set of 3D shapes will construct the composite Test Figure.

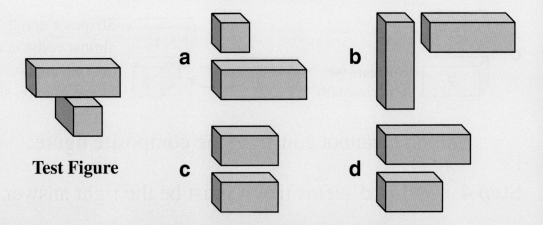

Test Figure

Method A - Putting Shapes Together

Step 1 - Option **a** looks unlikely to work.

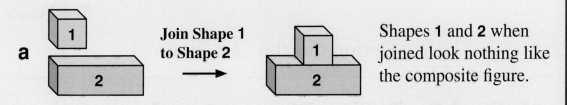

Join Shape 1 to Shape 2

Shapes **1** and **2** when joined look nothing like the composite figure.

Option **a** cannot construct the composite figure.

Step 2 - Option **b** again looks unlikely to work.

We have to imagine the shapes rotating and moving into new positions in order to check this option. They have been numbered for clarity.

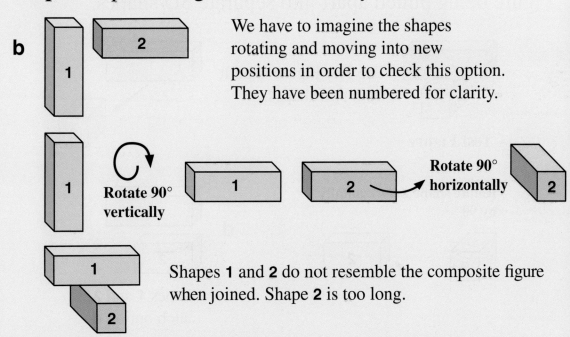

Rotate 90° vertically

Rotate 90° horizontally

Shapes **1** and **2** do not resemble the composite figure when joined. Shape **2** is too long.

Option **b** cannot construct the composite figure.

Step 3 - Option **c** almost seems to work. One of
the shapes needs to be rotated to check it.

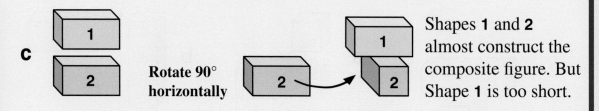

c   Rotate 90°
horizontal

Shapes **1** and **2**
almost construct the
composite figure. But
Shape **1** is too short.

Option **c** cannot construct the composite figure.

Step 4 - Option **d** seems like it must be the right answer.

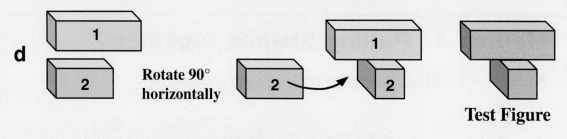

d   Rotate 90°
horizontally

Test Figure

Option **d** is the Test Figure.

Method B - Pulling Shapes Apart

Another way of solving the problem is to imagine the Test
Figure being pulled apart into separate 3D shapes.

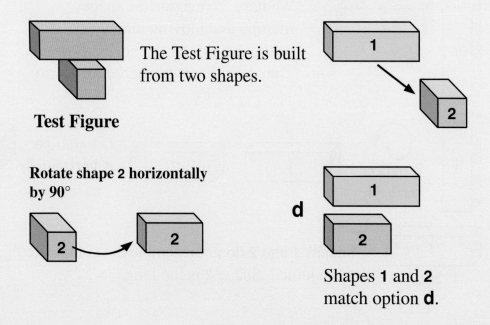

The Test Figure is built
from two shapes.

Test Figure

Rotate shape 2 horizontally
by 90°

d

Shapes **1** and **2**
match option **d**.

This shows that option **d** constructs the composite figure.

© 2016 Stephen Curran ae

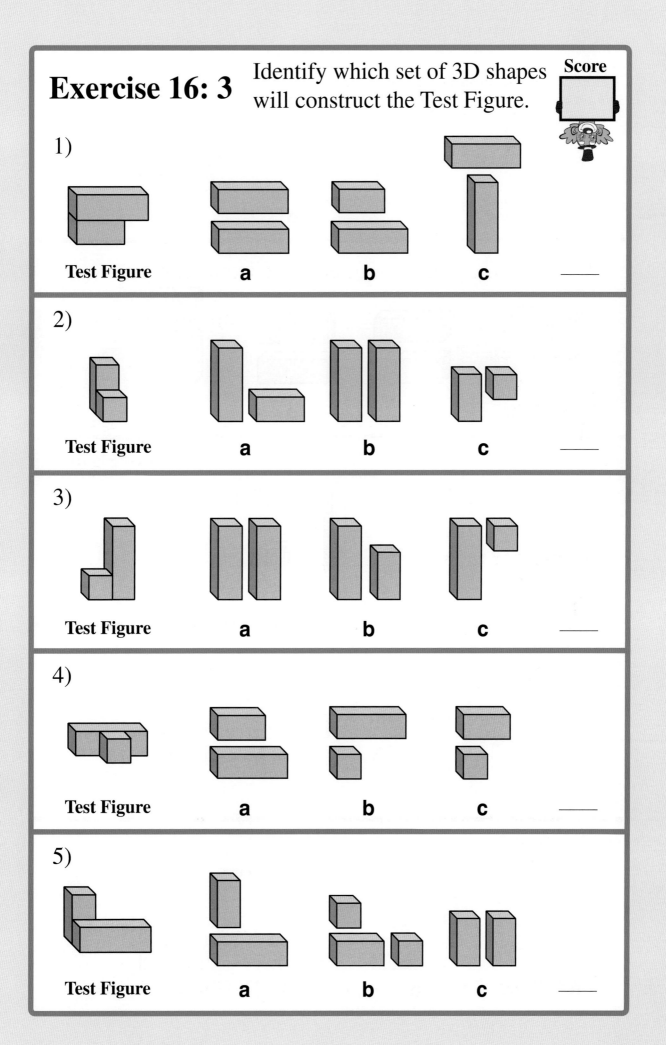

Exercise 16: 3

Identify which set of 3D shapes will construct the Test Figure.

1)

Test Figure   a   b   c   _____

2)

Test Figure   a   b   c   _____

3)

Test Figure   a   b   c   _____

4)

Test Figure   a   b   c   _____

5)

Test Figure   a   b   c   _____

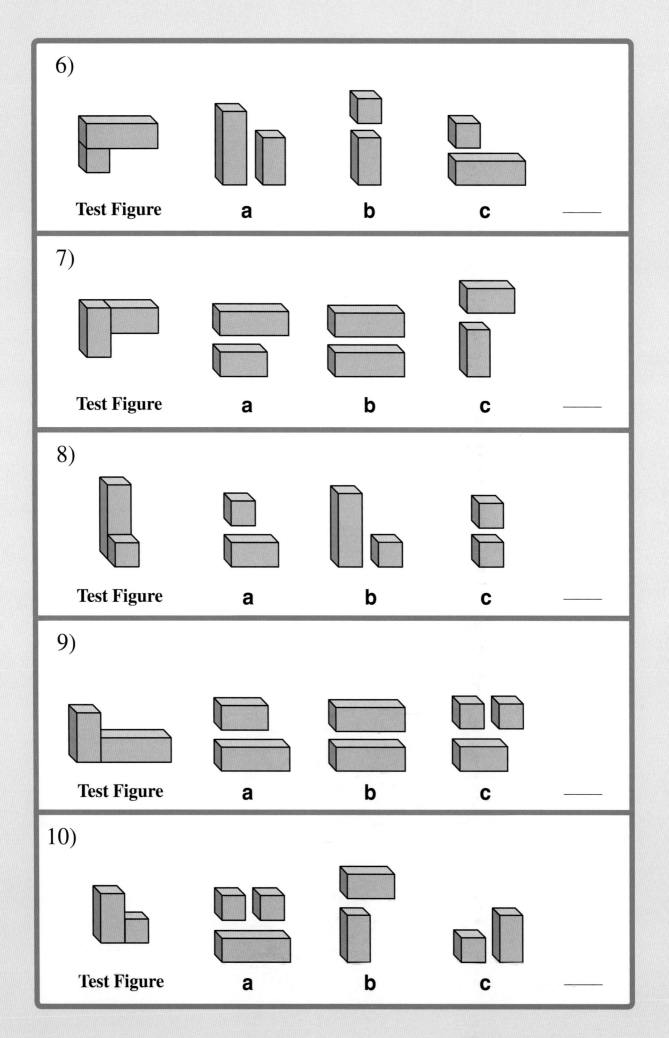

6)

Test Figure   **a**   **b**   **c**   ____

7)

Test Figure   **a**   **b**   **c**   ____

8)

Test Figure   **a**   **b**   **c**   ____

9)

Test Figure   **a**   **b**   **c**   ____

10)

Test Figure   **a**   **b**   **c**   ____

3. Rotating Figures

A 3D composite figure constructed from Cubes and Cuboids can be rotated **90°** on any one of two planes:

3D Vertical Rotation

A 3D figure can be rotated vertically by **90°** in either a clockwise or anticlockwise direction.

Rotate anticlockwise by 90°   **Rotate clockwise by 90°**

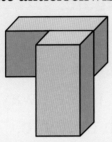 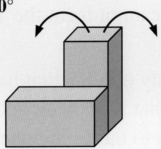 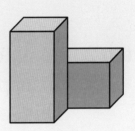

3D Horizontal Rotation

A 3D figure can be rotated horizontally (on a horizontal or flat plane) to the left or to the right by **90°**.

Rotate to the left by 90°   **Rotate to the right by 90°**

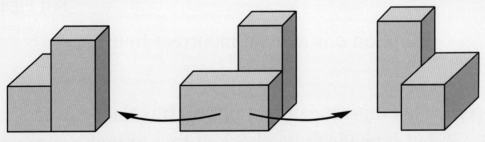

Example: | Identify which figure has been rotated to make the Test Figure.

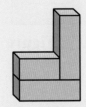 a 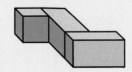 b 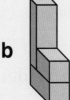 c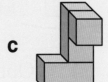

Test Figure

Step 1 - Look for any options that give the wrong 3D figure even if they are rotated. The most obvious option is **a**.

a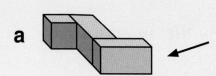

Compare this with the Test Figure. There is a single block in this figure.

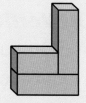

Test Figure

Option **a** cannot form the Test Figure.

Step 2 - Look for any options that have incorrect shapes or shapes that have been added or taken away. This seems to have happened with option **c**.

c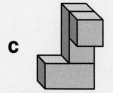

Compare this with the Test Figure. This shape should be taller.

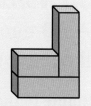

Test Figure

Option **c** is also an incorrect figure.

Step 3 - This must mean that option **b** is the answer but it needs to be checked first to make sure.

b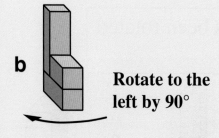

Rotate to the left by 90°

We can rotate option **b** and compare this with the Test Figure.

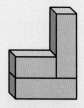

Test Figure

Option **b** is identical to the Test Figure.
Therefore option **b** is the correct answer.

Exercise 16: 4

Identify which figure has been rotated to make the Test Figure.

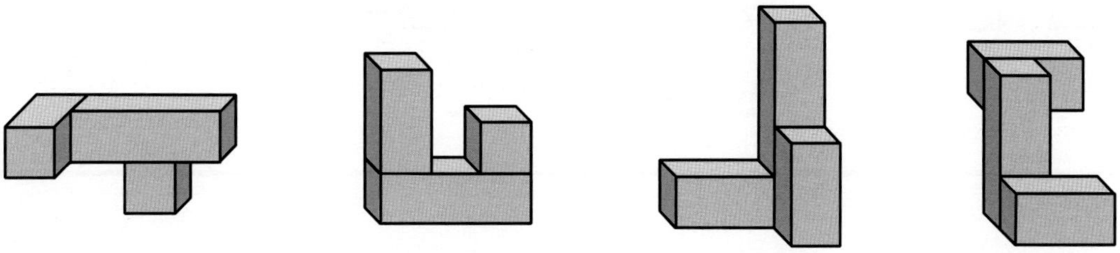

a　　　　**b**　　　　**c**　　　　**d**

1)

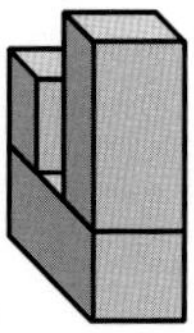

Test Figure

Answer ____

2)

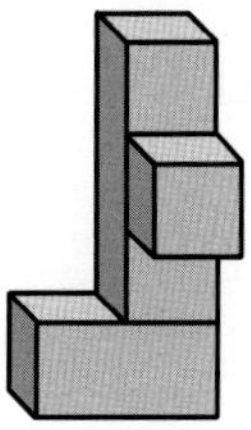

Test Figure

Answer ____

3)

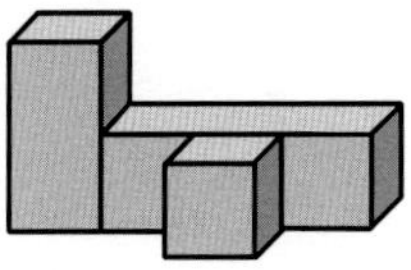

Test Figure

Answer ____

4)

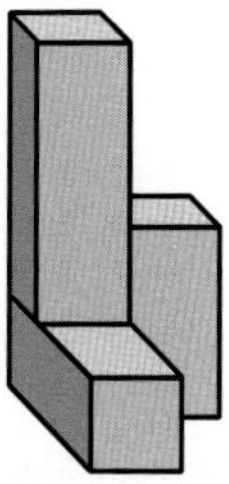

Test Figure

Answer ____

5)

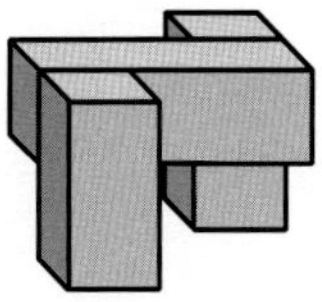

Test Figure

Answer ____

6)

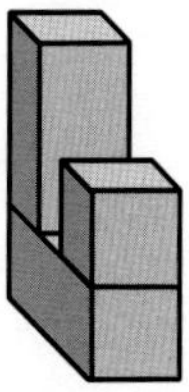

Test Figure

Answer ____

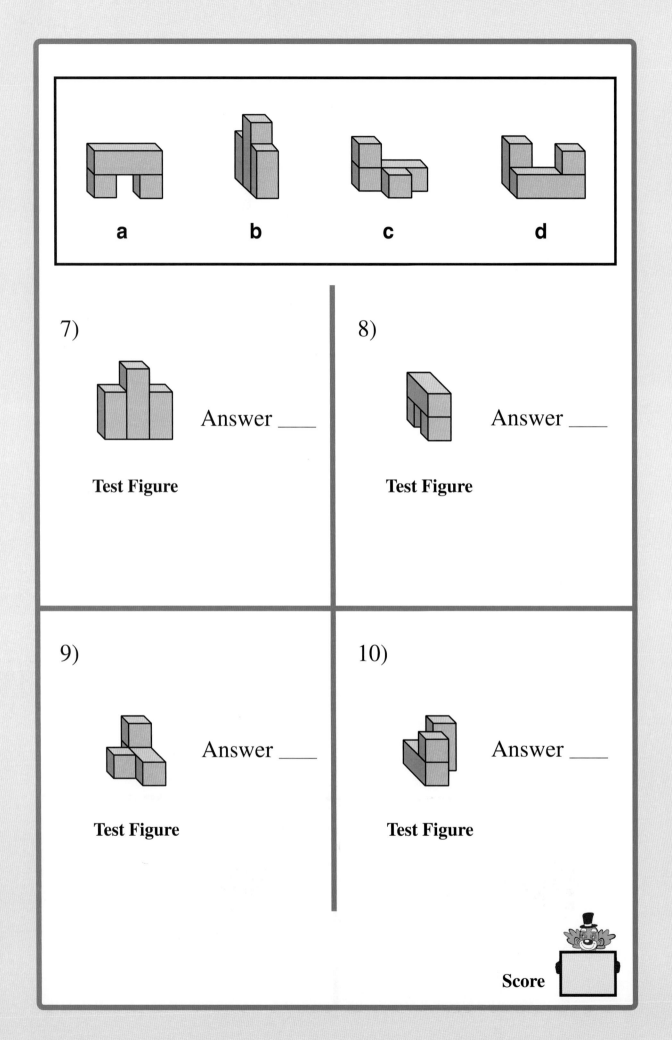

a   b   c   d

7)

Answer ____

Test Figure

8)

Answer ____

Test Figure

9)

Answer ____

Test Figure

10)

Answer ____

Test Figure

Score

44

© 2016 Stephen Curran

Answers

Chapter Fourteen
3D Rotation
Exercise 14: 1
1) **b**
2) **c**
3) **d**
4) **e**
5) **a**
6) **a**
7) **d**
8) **a**
9) **c**
10) **b**

Exercise 14: 2
1) Cone
2) Cube
3) Eraser
4) Cross
5) Cuboid
6) Triangular Prism
7) Steps
8) Cylinder
9) Square-based Pyramid
10) Bridge

Exercise 14: 3
1) **c**
2) **a**
3) **b**
4) **b**
5) **c**
6) **a**
7) **b**
8) **c**
9) **c**
10) **a**

Exercise 14: 4a
1) **a**
2) **c**
3) **b**
4) **c**
5) **c**

Exercise 14: 4b
6) **b**
7) **b**
8) **a**
9) **c**
10) **c**

Chapter Fifteen
Viewer Rotation
Exercise 15: 1
1) 6
2) 6
3) 2
4) 8
5) 5
6) 8
7) 7
8) 7
9) 10
10) 6

Exercise 15: 2
1) **c** - front
2) **a** - front
3) **d** - top or plan
4) **d** - front
5) **c** - rear
6) **b** - side
7) **c** - front
8) **a** - rear
9) **b** - side
10) **a** - top or plan

Answers

Exercise 15: 3
1) **c**
2) **c**
3) **d**
4) **a**
5) **c**
6) **b**
7) **b**
8) **c**
9) **a**
10) **c**

Exercise 15: 4
1) 6
2) 4
3) 10
4) 12
5) 8
6) 9
7) 10
8) 14
9) 12
10) 14

Chapter Sixteen
Rotational View
Exercise 16: 1
1) Square-based Pyramid
2) Octahedron
3) Triangular Prism
4) Wedge
5) Tetrahedron
6) Cuboid
7) Cylinder
8) Cone
9) Pentagonal Prism
10) Hexagonal Prism

Exercise 16: 2a
1) **a**
2) **d**
3) **d**
4) **c**
5) **c**

Exercise 16: 2b
6) **d**
7) **a**
8) **c**
9) **b**
10) **c**

Exercise 16: 3
1) **b**
2) **c**
3) **c**
4) **b**
5) **a**
6) **c**
7) **c**
8) **b**
9) **a**
10) **c**

Exercise 16: 4
1) **b**
2) **a**
3) **a**
4) **c**
5) **d**
6) **b**
7) **b**
8) **a**
9) **c**
10) **d**

PROGRESS CHARTS

14. 3D ROTATION

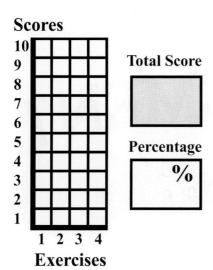

Scores

10 9 8 7 6 5 4 3 2 1

1 2 3 4
Exercises

Total Score

Percentage
%

15. VIEWER ROTATION

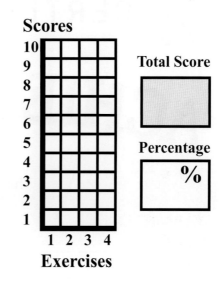

Scores

10 9 8 7 6 5 4 3 2 1

1 2 3 4
Exercises

Total Score

Percentage
%

16. ROTATIONAL VIEW

Scores

10 9 8 7 6 5 4 3 2 1

1 2 3 4
Exercises

Total Score

Percentage
%

Shade in your score for each exercise on the graphs. Add up for your total score.

For the average add up % and divide by 3

Overall Percentage
%

CERTIFICATE OF

ACHIEVEMENT

This certifies

_____

has successfully completed

11+ Non-verbal Reasoning
Year 3/4
WORKBOOK **3**

Overall percentage
score achieved ⬚ **%**

Comment _____

_____

Signed _____
(teacher/parent/guardian)

Date _____